MORE**COLOURING**
FOR CONTEMPLATION

Amber Hatch with Illustrations by **Alex Ogg**

WATKINS
Sharing Wisdom Since
1893

This edition first published in the UK and Ireland 2016 by
Watkins, an imprint of Watkins Media Limited
19 Cecil Court, London WC2N 4EZ

enquiries@watkinspublishing.com

Design and typography copyright © Watkins Media Limited 2016
Text copyright © Amber Hatch 2016
Illustrations copyright © Alex Ogg 2016

1 3 5 7 9 10 8 6 4 2

Designed by Clare Thorpe

Printed and bound in China

A CIP record for this book is available from the British Library

ISBN: 978-1-78028-976-2

www.watkinspublishing.com

CONTENTS

INTRODUCTION

If you have ever done any colouring, whether recently or years ago, you will know it is a soothing activity. When we continually bring our mind back to focus on a single object – in this case, the nib of the pen or pencil as it marks the page – then it begins to settle down. We become more absorbed in the task at hand, the mind becomes calmer, and worry and agitation start to slip away.

In our first book, *Colouring for Contemplation*, my husband Alex and I explored how colouring can be used as an opportunity to cultivate mindfulness. Mindfulness is different to calm – it's a quality of expansive awareness of our experiences moment to moment. Mindfulness doesn't come automatically; you need to make an effort to remember to do it. Mindfulness helps us to live life more fully and allows us to make conscious decisions about the way we act. It leads to a deeper connection with ourselves, other people and the world around us.

DEVELOPING CONNECTION

In this book, we decided to use colouring to explore how we can further develop this connection. You can use this book as an extension of the ideas in *Colouring for Contemplation*, or you can dive in right here.

We have used the following four qualities as a framework for thinking about how we relate to ourselves and the wider world.

Love

Compassion

Joy

Equanimity

Most people will know what it is like to experience love, compassion and joy. Equanimity may be less familiar; it is a quality of balance and stability that keeps us grounded.

The four qualities are grouped together and known in Buddhism as the *Brahma Viharas*, or 'Divine Abodes'. It is taught that, just like mindfulness, these feelings can actually be *cultivated*. This means that if we practise them, we can actually feel *more* love, *more* compassion, *more* joy and *more* equanimity. Not just towards people that we already like; we can learn how to extend these feelings towards more challenging people too. This enriches our relationships by bringing happiness to both ourselves and others, and helps to break down the barriers that limit us.

HOW TO USE THIS BOOK

In this book we explore these qualities through words and images, and also through meditation and reflection.

If you like, you can use this book to take you on a journey of inner exploration. In each section we have selected eight quotations from speakers around the world that can help us towards a deeper understanding of the theme. They are chosen to help conjure aspects of each feeling. Alex has drawn images that interpret these quotations. As you colour and complete the images, you may like to consider how your work has influenced the way the picture relates to the teaching.

At the end of each section you'll find a guided meditation, adapted from traditional Buddhist teaching, which can help you develop these states further. By intentionally raising each empathic quality, you can learn to deepen it. Becoming familiar with a feeling through meditation makes it easier to incorporate it in everyday life.

In the 'Reflections' section you can consider how you may have deepened your understanding and capacity for positive qualities. This is not a set of instructions to be followed rigidly, but an opportunity for gentle contemplation at your own pace. This is followed by practical suggestions for incorporating the themes into your daily life, where you can reap the practical rewards of deepening your empathy.

There is also a suggestion for your journal, if you keep one. A 'Notes' page allows space for trying out colours and techniques, or for jotting down your thoughts and ideas.

You may be keen to simply get stuck in and get colouring. That's fine! Alex has designed the images to be playful and provocative, with differing levels of challenge. We hope you like them.

TECHNIQUE

There are no rules with colouring but sometimes it's helpful to have some pointers to help you get started or for when you want to try out new ideas.

- Mix and match! Pencil crayons, marker pens, fineliners, watercolour pencils, glitter and gel pens can all be used to different effect.
- You may like to try limiting your colours to a small selection, for example all blues and greys, or autumnal colours.
- Use a light touch with pencil crayons, and gradually build up the colour in certain areas to create texture.
- Create different shades by blending two different pencil crayon colours together.
- If you are pressing hard on the page, or using very inky pens, slide a sheet of paper between the pages to protect the picture on the following page from bleed or indentation.
- Make mistakes! Exploring new areas always results in the odd wrong turn.
- Don't forget to take a break every 20 minutes or so to avoid straining your hand and wrist. You can use this as an opportunity for meditation.

LOVE

The word love has many shades of meaning. The love we mean here is not a yearning, needy kind of love, but one that replenishes both giver and receiver. It starts with a feeling of friendliness, of warmth and kindness. A sense of goodwill and well-wishing. This kind of love doesn't ask for anything in return. Even if it is not there all the time, most of us know what it is like to feel this kind of easy love for our friends and family.

What you may not know is that we can actually learn to amplify it. We can do this by recognizing it, valuing it and calling it up. When we direct this love towards ourselves, we become more accepting of who we are. With this base of love for ourselves, we are better able to feel love for others.

We can learn to increase the love we already feel for those we care for. We can make our love stronger, more consistent and, ultimately, unconditional. We can also learn to direct our goodwill towards people outside of our immediate circle. We can extend our warmth to more and more people, until it is boundless.

May we all be well and happy.

'Love does not consist of gazing at each other,
but in looking outward together in the same direction.'

ANTOINE DE SAINT-EXUPÉRY
FRENCH WRITER AND AVIATOR

(1900–1944)

'My bounty is as boundless as the sea,
My love as deep. The more I give to thee,
The more I have, for both are infinite.'

WILLIAM SHAKESPEARE
ENGLISH PLAYWRIGHT

(1564–1616)

'A small house will hold a hundred friends.'

AFRICAN PROVERB

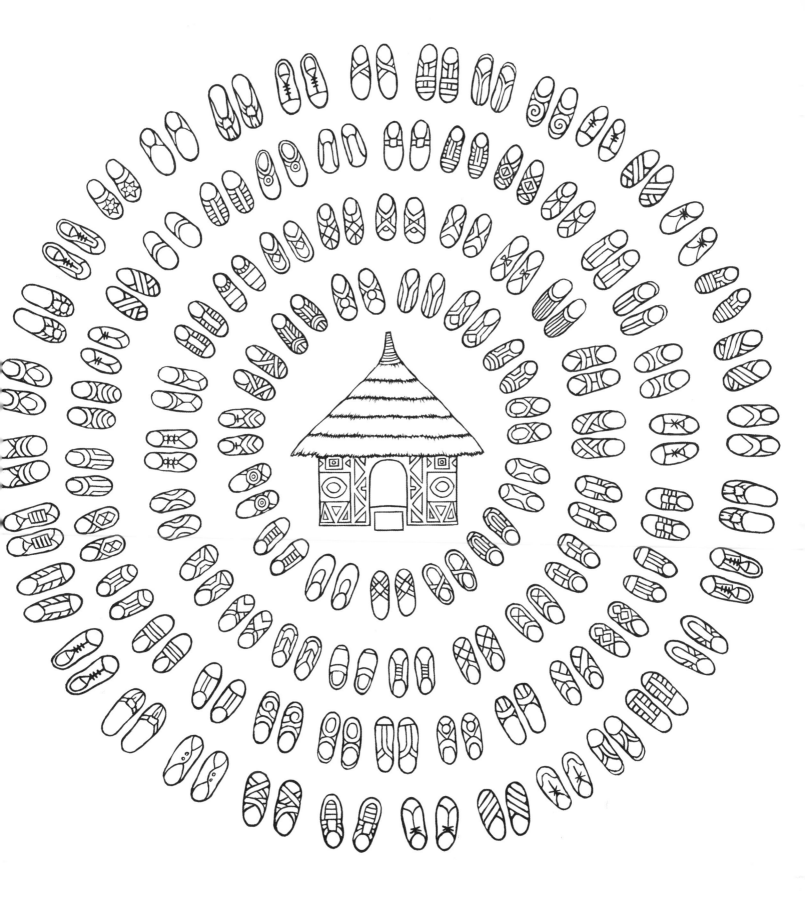

'Love grows by giving. The love we give away is the only love we keep. The only way to retain love is to give it away.'

ELBERT HUBBARD

AMERICAN WRITER AND PHILOSOPHER

(1856–1915)

'But with proper practice, from an ordinary level of affection we can develop an unbiased universal love, in which we don't care what other people's faith is, their nationality, or social status – so long as they are human beings, they are our brothers and sisters.'

HIS HOLINESS THE 14TH DALAI LAMA

(B. 1935)

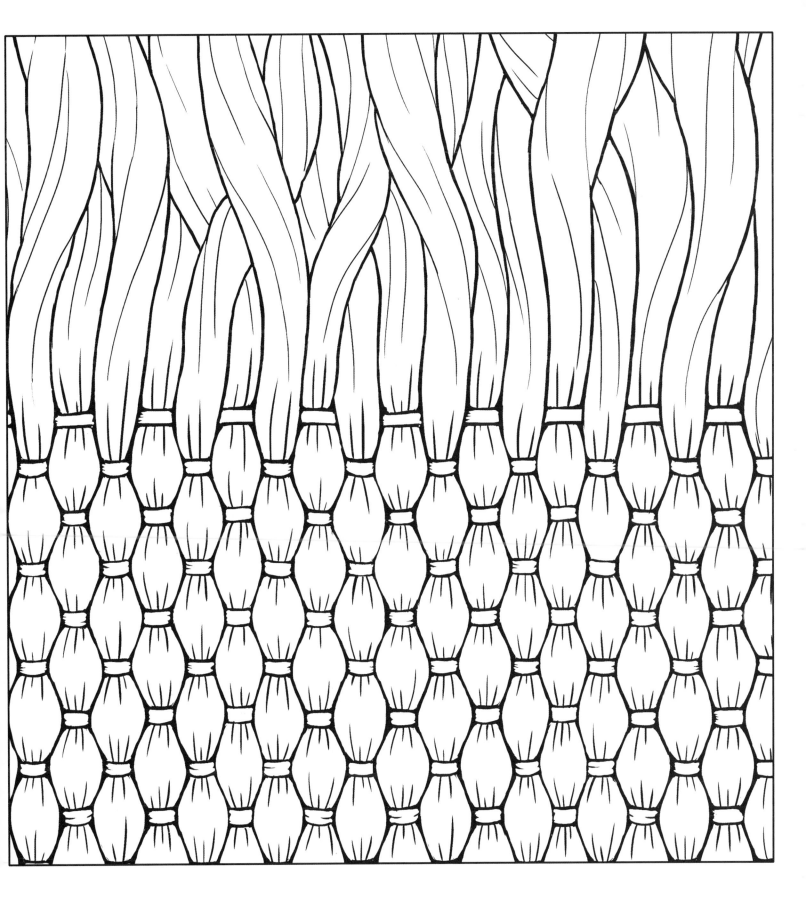

'Blessed is the influence of one true,
loving human soul on another.'

GEORGE ELIOT

ENGLISH NOVELIST

(1819–1880)

MEDITATION ON LOVE

Find a comfortable, well-supported spot to sit. Close your eyes and take a moment to locate yourself in your body. Pay attention to how your breath rises and falls.

Before you can send love outwards, you need to direct love towards yourself. Silently, start to repeat the phrase: 'May I be well and happy.' You can also try using different sayings to find what resonates with you. For example, 'May I be at ease.' 'May I be free from trouble.' 'May I be safe.'

You may find it easier to conjure a feeling of wellbeing towards yourself through visualization. Imagine the warmth spreading around and through you as if you are in a sauna. Or that the loving feeling is a warm, drizzling rain that gradually soaks through your clothes into your skin.

Now try directing it outwards. Start by sending the loving feeling to other people or creatures in the room where you sit. Then include the whole building. Radiate outwards so that your love expands to include the neighbourhood. Now extend it to the town or city. Widen your circle to include the country. And the continent. And now the entire world . . . and beyond.

REFLECTIONS

The quotations and images in this section have explored the quality of love and, in particular, how we can cultivate warmth and kindness, not just to one or two particular people but in ever-increasing circles, without bounds. Use this opportunity to consider how you may have been inspired by these quotations and images, or perhaps by other events in your life right now.

REVIEWING YOUR WORK

Take a few moments to consider the following questions – you may want to note down your answers in your journal:

- Which pictures or quotations particularly resonated with you?
- Which picture best sums up your understanding of love?
- Did you find any of the ideas difficult?
- Did you notice feeling love towards any particular person or thing when colouring?
- Did the teachings have any impact on the way you chose to colour the image?
- Were there limits to your loving feelings – perhaps towards yourself or, maybe, to others?

NURTURING LOVE IN YOUR DAILY LIFE

Practising loving acceptance towards ourselves is just as important as developing it towards others. It can also feel hard at times. Take time to notice your own desire to be happy, and wish yourself well. If it seems difficult, try imagining yourself as a small child, or perhaps a vulnerable animal, and send yourself warm wishes.

Make time for your own wellbeing by doing activities that make you feel nurtured. Whether that's spending an afternoon on the sofa with a book, or arranging to meet with a friend.

Notice the love you already feel towards friends and family. Try to spot any circumstances when you withhold that love, perhaps when they are not behaving as you prefer. Try to make your love unconditional.

When you are out among strangers, take a moment to notice individuals around you. Recognize that they want to be happy, just like you.

Say hello to someone you don't know. Or if you normally say hello, why not ask them, 'How are you today?'

Spread kindness through your actions – help somebody with their shopping bags, ask a neighbour if they need anything from the shop, make a coffee for a colleague, warm your children's pyjamas on the radiator before bedtime.

IN YOUR JOURNAL

Make a note of times when you have felt love and warmth towards someone. You may also want to record when it has been difficult. Consider if there are ways to outwardly express your warmth of feeling.

NOTES ... DOODLES ... IDEAS ... SCRIBBLES ... THOUGHTS ...

COMPASSION

When love finds suffering it manifests as compassion. Compassion is often confused with pity, but the two are quite different. When we pity, we protect ourselves by keeping separate. We look down on the person in pain and stay disconnected.

Compassion, however, comes from *sharing* suffering. We recognize someone else's pain, and we allow ourselves to feel it too. This is true whether we are considering ourselves or other people. Feeling compassion for ourselves means acknowledging and allowing ourselves to be in pain, and holding that pain carefully in our hands, perhaps in the way we might hold a trembling rabbit.

It can be difficult to feel compassion because we have to acknowledge weakness and vulnerability. It's tempting to turn away. We may worry that looking and feeling will leave us depleted. We may not want to admit our own pain either. It can feel easier to deny it.

But when compassion has love driving it forwards, with a foundation of equanimity, facing up to the truth of suffering becomes liberating. It is the denial of suffering that diminishes us.

May we all be free from suffering.

'No act of kindness, no matter how small,
is ever wasted.'

AESOP
ANCIENT GREEK FABULIST AND STORYTELLER
(c. 620–564 BCE)

'Compassion is not at all weak.
It is the strength that arises out of seeing
the true nature of suffering in the world.'

SHARON SALZBERG

AMERICAN AUTHOR AND MEDITATION TEACHER

(B. 1952)

'You have not lived today
until you have done something for
someone who can never repay you.'

JOHN BUNYAN

ENGLISH WRITER AND PREACHER

(1628–1688)

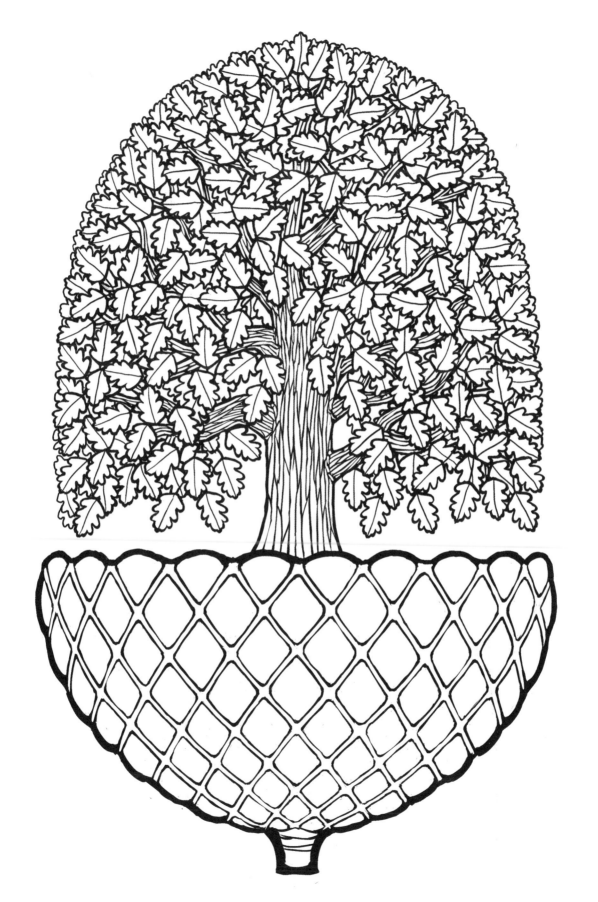

'True benevolence, or compassion, extends itself through the whole of existence and sympathises with the distress of every creature capable of sensation.'

JOSEPH ADDISON
ENGLISH WRITER AND POLITICIAN
(1672–1719)

'The more we know, the better we forgive.
Those who feel deeply feel for all living beings.'

MADAME DE STAËL
FRENCH WRITER AND CRITIC
(1766–1817)

'If any man has a hundred sheep,
and one of them has gone astray,
does he not leave the ninety-nine
on the mountains and go and search
for the one that is straying?'

MATTHEW 18:12, NEW TESTAMENT

'You can hold yourself back from the sufferings of the world, that is something you are free to do and it accords with your nature, but perhaps this very holding back is the one suffering you could avoid.'

FRANZ KAFKA
CZECH GERMAN-LANGUAGE NOVELIST AND WRITER
(1883–1924)

'The simplest acts of kindness are by far more powerful than a thousand heads bowing in prayer.'

MAHATMA GANDHI

INDIAN ACTIVIST AND INDEPENDENCE LEADER

(1869–1948)

MEDITATION ON COMPASSION

Find a comfortable, well-supported spot to sit. Close your eyes and take a moment to locate yourself in your body. Pay attention to how your breath rises and falls.

Start by looking inwards and notice if there is any pain within yourself. This may be physical or emotional pain (which may also manifest physically perhaps as an ache or tightness in your chest or belly). Hold that pain tenderly and examine it. Allow yourself to explore and feel it. Breathe into it with a soothing, healing breath. Some pains are inevitable, but we can choose to lighten them by accepting them or add to them by resisting. Say to yourself, 'May I be free from unnecessary suffering.'

Now look outwards and bring to mind someone else who is suffering. Hold their pain in your hands and examine it. Allow yourself to know their pain. Direct the following phrase towards them, 'May they be free from suffering'.

Now expand this feeling in an ever-increasing circle, bringing to mind all beings that suffer – whether now or in the past or in the future. Include those you love and also those you find difficult. Everybody wants to be free from suffering. Send your compassion to all of them, without exclusion or limits.

REFLECTIONS

The pictures in this section have explored the quality of compassion, how it can sometimes be difficult and scary, and yet powerful and liberating for both giver and receiver.

Take a few moments to think about how these quotations and images may have resonated with you. The following questions and ideas will help you consider the quality and may encourage you to find more compassion in your life.

REVIEWING YOUR WORK

Take a few moments to consider the following questions – you may want to note down your answers in your journal:

- Which pictures did you enjoy colouring the most? Why?
- Which ones most evoked the spirit of compassion?
- Did you find any of the pictures poignant? If so, how did that make you feel?
- What colours do you feel most express compassion?
- Can you think of any place where your understanding of the quotations or the image changed as you worked on the picture?
- When you did the meditation, did you find it harder to direct compassion towards some people compared to others? If so, why?

LETTING IN COMPASSION IN YOUR DAILY LIFE

Trying to ignore or get away from pain can make it worse. The next time you feel some physical discomfort, try to explore it, allowing it to be how it is. Breathe into the discomfort. Make it welcome. Allow it to come and go in its own time.

When a friend or acquaintance tells you about some trouble they are experiencing, try to empathize by really listening and understanding their difficulty. Don't immediately offer advice or ways to solve the issue. Be with them in their difficulty. Share it.

Sometimes reading about troubles in the newspapers can be overwhelming. The way we may try to protect ourselves is to shut ourselves off from others. Consider how much news you consume, and for what purpose. Be open to what you read and hear.

When you notice a compassionate impulse, act on it – perhaps by buying a hot drink for someone who is homeless or giving a donation to charity, for example.

When you next hear a crying baby, be open to the suffering of both the child and the parent. Offer them a smile and your understanding.

IN YOUR JOURNAL

Make a note of any pain in your life, and consider how you can accept it. Think of people that you care about, and also those that you find difficult, and consider what pain they may be suffering. Allow yourself to acknowledge that too. You may naturally think of ways that you could help relieve that pain, or you may not. Either way is fine.

NOTES ... DOODLES ... IDEAS ...
SCRIBBLES ... THOUGHTS ...

JOY

Just as love turns to compassion when it finds suffering, so love naturally turns to joy when it looks upon happiness. When we love people, we celebrate their successes. This feeling is sometimes called *sympathetic joy*, because it is about sharing joy with others – just like a mother watching her child take his first steps. Joy doesn't run out. Sharing our own and other people's joy *multiplies* it. The more we look for opportunities to feel joy, the more we have it. With practice, even small things begin to spark joy.

Sometimes, it can be hard to share other people's joy. If we feel out of love and disconnected from other people, their successes may make us feel angry and resentful. Or, if despite being pleased for them, their successes make us feel inadequate, then we may not be directing enough love towards ourselves – perhaps we find it difficult to experience our own joy.

It is even harder to share the joy of those that we find challenging, or that are causing harm to others. By opening our hearts to joy wherever it appears, we are greatly expanding our own capacity to feel happiness.

May we all experience joy.

'There is not one blade of grass,
there is no colour in this world that is
not intended to make us rejoice.'

JOHN CALVIN
FRENCH THEOLOGIAN AND PASTOR

(1509–1564)

'I adore Life. What do all the fools matter and all
the stupidity. They do matter but somehow for me
they cannot touch the body of Life. Life is marvellous.
I want to be deeply rooted in it – to live – to expand –
to breathe in it – to rejoice – to share it.
To give and to be asked for Love.'

KATHERINE MANSFIELD
NEW ZEALAND WRITER
(1888–1923)

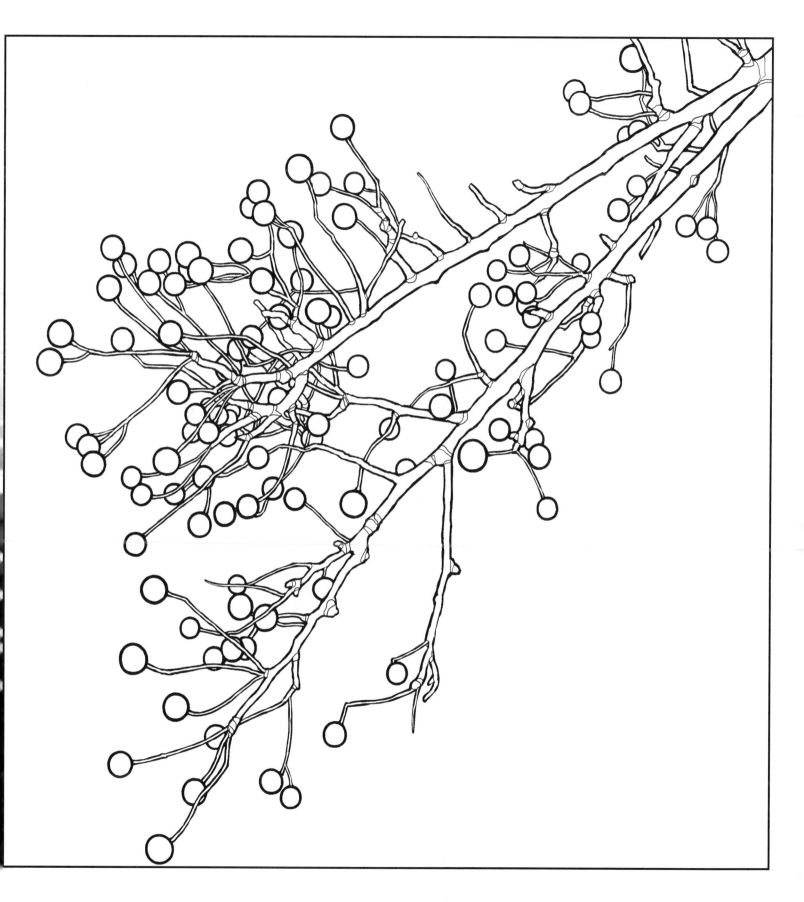

'While with an eye made quiet by the power
Of harmony, and the deep power of joy,
We see into the life of things.'

WILLIAM WORDSWORTH
ENGLISH POET

(1770–1850)

'Being human means throwing your whole life on the scale of destiny when need be, all the while rejoicing in every sunny day and every beautiful cloud.'

ROSA LUXEMBURG
POLISH-BORN GERMAN REVOLUTIONARY AND PHILOSOPHER
(1871–1919)

'There is nothing in the world so irresistibly contagious as laughter and good humour.'

CHARLES DICKENS
ENGLISH NOVELIST AND SOCIAL CRITIC
(1812–1870)

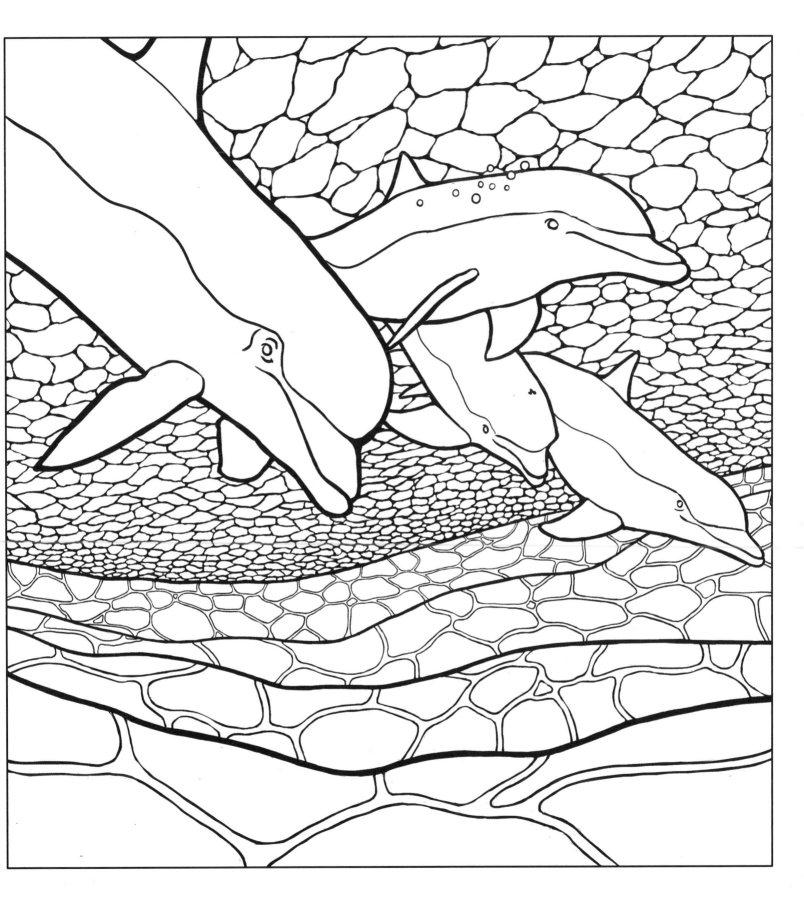

'For those of us who have not gotten into that situation, we are able to see that happiness can come from every direction. Happiness can come from the west, from the east, from the north and the south, from above, and from below. And if we are committed to just one idea of happiness, we block all the other avenues.'

THICH NHAT HANH
VIETNAMESE ZEN MASTER AND PEACE ACTIVIST

(B. 1926)

MEDITATION ON JOY

Find a comfortable, well-supported spot to sit. Close your eyes and take a moment to locate yourself in your body. Pay attention to how your breath rises and falls.

Bring to mind a good friend or family member who has some good fortune. Notice your own gladness at their happiness. Open your heart to their success by dwelling in it and amplifying it. Now recall some achievement or good fortune of your own and allow yourself to feel joy and gratitude. It could be something you have done well, or some good luck, or even simply a good-hearted aspiration.

Now bring to mind someone you feel neutral about. Try to bring to mind some happiness they experience – it could be real or, if you don't know of any, imagined. Share in their joy, and feel grateful for this happiness too.

Now look at someone whom you find difficult. Bring to mind some achievement or good fortune for them. Try to acknowledge their happiness too, without resentment.

Now extend this to all beings everywhere, allowing yourself to be open to the joy of all beings, without bounds or limits.

REFLECTIONS

This section has considered joy – and particularly the joy that comes from celebrating the success of others. By opening ourselves to the experience of joy from any quarter, we are exponentially increasing our potential for happiness.

Spend some time thinking about how these quotations and images may have evoked joy for you. The following questions and ideas will help you to see if you can find more joy in your life.

REVIEWING YOUR WORK

Take a few moments to consider the following questions – you may want to note down your answers in your journal:

- Did colouring any of these pictures evoke joy? Which ones?
- What colours make you feel joyful and happy – where could you add more of that colour to your life?
- Can you notice what quality of mind precedes joy? Is it the same every time?
- Is there a link between your level of awareness, through meditation, and your ability to appreciate joy?
- Can you think of any other quotes or sayings that you know which conjure feelings of gladness?
- What could you draw to depict that saying?

FINDING JOY IN YOUR DAILY LIFE

Rejoice in your own success. Take time to notice when you have done something well, and congratulate yourself.

Make an effort to ask how people are doing, so that you know what's going on in their life. You can't feel happy for them if they don't have any opportunity to share their success.

When you feel pleased for a friend, take a minute to dwell in that feeling. Learn how it feels so it is easier to conjure at other times.

Notice what happens when someone you dislike has good fortune. How do you feel? If you feel diminished and tight inside, notice that, and see if you might be able to let it go.

Happiness does not necessarily sit comfortably with our worldly view of 'success'. Spending time with our loved ones can bring far more joy. Make time for a relaxed conversation with your partner, or indulge in playtime with a child.

Look around you for joy in unusual places – perhaps the sight of a plant breaking through a crack in the pavement, or birdsong in the morning. When we open our hearts, we can find joy all around.

IN YOUR JOURNAL

Jot down any times in the last few days when you have felt gladdened. Notice what triggered that feeling. See if you can spot other opportunities to feel joy. Write a list of all the things that bring you joy.

NOTES ... DOODLES ... IDEAS ... SCRIBBLES ... THOUGHTS ...

EQUANIMITY

If love is a tree that grows up and reaches out into the world, then equanimity is the root system that steadies and sustains it. Without equanimity our tree would be parched by the hot sun and knocked over by the wind.

Equanimity is the quality that enables us to continue to love, feel compassion and joy, even when it is difficult. Perhaps our love is not returned, or suffering seems too painful to bear. Equanimity protects us by keeping us balanced and grounded. It allows us to love without an agenda, feel compassion without slipping into despair, feel joy without clinging. Having equanimity means we are not ruffled by things beyond our control. We can call it up when we notice any resistance to what is happening in our lives by consciously allowing things to be as they are.

Equanimity is not indifference. It does not turn away. It allows us to look for longer and more deeply. Equanimity underpins the other three qualities – love, compassion and joy – enabling them to extend further outwards. It becomes especially important when we turn our attention to a person who presents us with a lot of challenge – perhaps someone who is suffering, but is unaware of their own pain.

May we all be grounded and sustained by equanimity.

'No lake so still but it has its wave.
No circle so perfect but that it has its blur.
I would change things for you if I could;
As I can't you must take them as they are.'

CONFUCIUS

CHINESE PHILOSOPHER

(551–479 BCE)

'How is it they live in such harmony, the billions of stars, when most men can barely go a minute without declaring war in their minds?'

ST THOMAS AQUINAS
ITALIAN PRIEST, THEOLOGIAN AND PHILOSOPHER
(1224/5–1274)

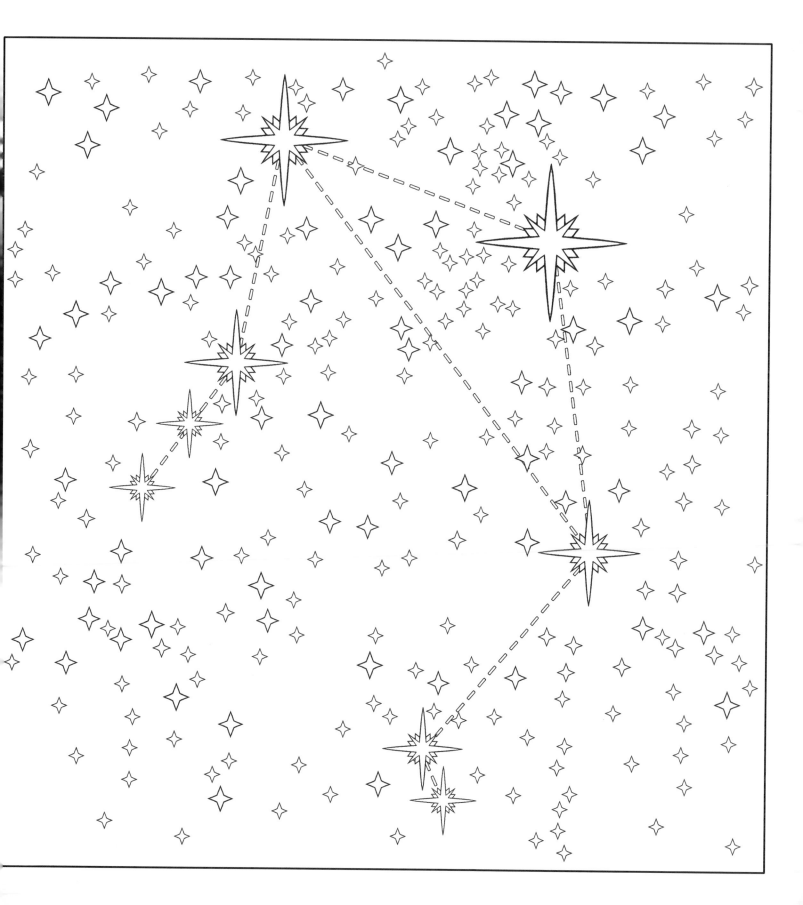

'If a man going down into a river,
swollen and swiftly flowing,
is carried away by the current –
how can he help others across?'

GAUTAMA BUDDHA
INDIAN SPIRITUAL LEADER

(c. 600–300 BCE)

'If you can meet with Triumph and Disaster
And treat those two impostors just the same . . . '

RUDYARD KIPLING

ENGLISH NOVELIST AND POET

(1865–1936)

'If you are irritated by every rub,
how will your mirror be polished?'

RUMI
SUFI POET AND PHILOSOPHER
(1207–1273)

'You always own the option of having no opinion.
There is never any need to get worked up or
to trouble your soul about things you can't control.
These things are not asking to be judged by you.
Leave them alone.'

MARCUS AURELIUS
ROMAN EMPEROR

(121–180 CE)

'Calm soul of all things! Make it mine
To feel, amid the city's jar,
That there abides a peace of thine,
Man did not make, and cannot mar.'

MATTHEW ARNOLD

ENGLISH POET

(1822–1888)

'You are the sky.
Everything else – it's just the weather.'

PEMA CHÖDRÖN
AMERICAN TIBETAN BUDDHIST

(B. 1936)

MEDITATION ON EQUANIMITY

Find a comfortable, well-supported spot to sit. Close your eyes and take a moment to locate yourself in your body. Pay attention to how your breath rises and falls.

To help generate a sense of balance, first bring to mind someone you feel neutral towards. Someone whose life you don't want to influence or interfere with. Try to raise a sense of connection and well-wishing towards them, while at the same time recognizing that they are responsible for their own happiness. Notice the sense of calm and allowing.

Next direct your thoughts to a good friend. Send them warmth, yet at the same time, allow them too, to be as they are.

Now consider someone you find challenging. Can you allow this person to be responsible for their own happiness? Can you allow them to be how they are without feeling angry or agitated? Try to direct love or compassion towards them, from a place of calm and serenity in yourself. It does not matter if they don't accept or return it.

Lastly, turn this calm acceptance towards yourself. Acknowledge where you are right now. Suffuse the good feelings that you send yourself with patience and acceptance.

REFLECTIONS

The pictures and teachings in this section have focused on equanimity. They evoke a state of mind that remains steady and open, even when events are intense or not as we prefer.

Accepting events without resistance is a state of letting go. By giving up control, we are not diminished, but in fact cultivating a much deeper power. True strength lies in allowing things to be as they are. Taking action to change them is then optional.

REVIEWING YOUR WORK

Have a think about the following questions:

- Which quotation or image most evoked the quality of equanimity for you?
- Were any of the images or sayings challenging? Why?
- When did you find it easiest to maintain equanimity? When was it hard?
- Did you find yourself using a particular colour palette? Which colours make you feel calm and safe?
- Colouring naturally calms the mind, which is a good base for equanimity. Were there any times when you felt particularly calm?
- Can you transfer this calm into other areas of your life?

CULTIVATING EQUANIMITY IN YOUR DAILY LIFE

Recognizing the quality of equanimity is the first step towards cultivating it. Take time to notice the feeling when it arises naturally.

Spend some time in nature. Whichever season it is there will always be growth and decay, coming and going. You don't need to look far to find an example of this. Notice how nature accepts these changes without complaint.

Equanimity often follows understanding. The next time you encounter someone being grumpy or rude, consider what led to them acting like that. You may not guess right, but acknowledging that this behaviour has a cause makes it easier to take less personally.

If you feel yourself becoming agitated or angry, take a moment to breathe in, and find that calm space inside you, before you react.

Practising equanimity can be harder with people you know well. If your equanimity slips, revisit the situation a little later (without judgement) to see how it might have been different. When you have found more balance, make an effort to reconnect with the person.

IN YOUR JOURNAL

Jot down some things in nature that evoke the spirit of harmony and balance. If you have a challenging situation to deal with, note down how you might deal with it with more equanimity. Imagine the outcome.

NOTES ... DOODLES ... IDEAS ...
SCRIBBLES ... THOUGHTS ...

ACKNOWLEDGEMENTS

Thanks again to our agent Jane Graham Maw, who makes it happen. Thank you to Jo Lal and everyone at Watkins who has worked so hard, and with such good humour, on this book and the last.

We are very grateful to all the people from Samatha who have helped us develop our understanding and practice of meditation, particularly our teachers: Terry, Charles and Seb. Thanks also to Terry for his comments on the text.

Thanks to our friends in Oxford who have looked after our kids and generally provided moral support as we worked on this book. Special thanks to Fern and David for lending Alex their back door key.

THE FOLLOWING QUOTES ARE REPRODUCED WITH KIND PERMISSION.

Page 14: *The writings of Mother Teresa of Calcutta* © by the Mother Teresa Centre, exclusive licensee throughout the world of the Missionaries of Charity for the works of Mother Teresa. Used with permission.

Page 22 Reprinted with permission from the office of His Holiness the 14th Dalai Lama.

Page 34 Sharon Salzberg, excerpt from *Loving Kindness: The Revolutionary Art of Happiness*, © 1995 by Sharon Salzberg. Reprinted by arrangement with The Permissions Company, Inc., on behalf of Shambala Publications Inc., Boulder, Colarado, www.shambhala.com

Page 60 Cardinal Ratzinger, *Salt of the Earth* © 1997. Reprinted with kind permission by Ignatius Press, San Francisco.

Page 68 From 'Love without Frontiers' by Thich Nhat Hanh, November 25, 2004. Reprinted with permission from the Mindfulness Bell #70 (Autumn 2015).

Page 90 From a dharma talk by Pema Chödrön at Gampo Abbey in 2008. Reprinted with permission from The Pema Chödrön Foundation.